CW00819530

DIGITAL JUSTICE ™

Story and Art
BY
PEPE MORENO

Dialogue — Doug Murray

Additional Design — Javier Romero

Art Assistant — Bob Fingerman

Batman Created by — Bob Kane

Pre-Press — Anaya Systems

Anaya Programmer — Vicente Sosa

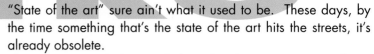

INTRO

"State of the art" sure ain't what it used to be. These days, by the time something that's the state of the art hits the streets, it's already obsolete.

That's an overwhelming change for the comic art medium. Between 1937, when the first all-original comic book came out, and the release of the first computer-generated comic in 1984, the tools used in the creation of comic art remained fairly stagnant.

That all changed with the introduction of the first *affordable* graphics-oriented computer. All of a sudden, we had a machine that could do anything. Most miraculously, that bottomless box of microchips and cathode rays has allowed our medium to grow — from the standpoint of technology — more in the ensuing five years than it did in the preceding forty-seven. At that time, I was the editor of a Midwest comic book company when a couple of old friends, Peter Gillis and Mike Saenz, showed me some rough printouts of a story that was produced entirely on a 128K Apple Macintosh computer, using but one disk drive. The artwork was chunky and brittle: it looked like some amphetamine addict had been given a box of zip-a-tone that suffered from a glandular disease. But the look was totally unique to comics. Within several months, we refined the look and the resulting effort — SHATTER — was one of the best-selling comics of the year. It completely astonished the folks over at Apple Computer, Inc., who never perceived such a use for their hardware.

We've come a long way in the past five years: the book you are now holding was produced on a Macintosh computer that has 64 times the internal memory, 400 times the storage capacity, about 8 times the speed, and hundreds of software packages. More important, DIGITAL JUSTICE takes advantage of different devices that, five years ago, were barely dreamed of for the home or studio: computer-aided design, 3-D imaging programs, high-resolution and direct-to-film printers, graphics scanners, and color. A whole lot of color. In fact, there's the potential for more than 16 million colors.

Back then, naysayers and technophobes looked at the end result and, seeing only its shortcomings, declared the computer useless in the creation of comic art. Since that time, that bottomless box has become so useful it is now almost invisible: artists have been using their machines to generate special effects, designers have been doing their design work on-line, letterers have been creating their own fonts, and craftspeople have been coloring comics with a palette (and the resultant special effects) heretofore unknown in the medium. DC Comics even has its own in-house computer coloring department.

But in order to keep pressing ahead, every once in a while we find ourselves doing a *pure computer* project — one in which everything on the printed page was generated with a computer. This allows us to see how far we've come... and that brings us to Pepe Moreno.

Pepe is quite a well-known artist out in Europe: his five highly successful albums and graphic novels (two of which have been reprinted in the States thus far) have earned him a reputation as a solid craftsman and an innovator. They expose his own sense of energy and a unique world-view, both of which he has brought to DIGITAL JUSTICE.

Pepe wanted to turn cold computer technology into a warm "product" and to make the computer invisible. This is a formidable goal; there is a certain point an artist can reach wherein the end result no longer appears to be computer generated; at that point, the project will *appear* to be self-defeating.

His early experiences with the Commodore Amiga Computer and primitive art programs gave Pepe a head start on the color Macintosh II. In creating the movie-like look of DIGITAL JUSTICE, Pepe conceived and executed his work directly on the monitor with the electronic medium in mind. He used a wide variety of tools to bring the book to life: CAD programs, vector illustration, 3-D modeling, text effects, and such paint programs as Image Studio, Studio/8 and Photo Shop.

Pepe then arranges these images into panels, and then, using Quark Xpress, the panels are assembled into pages, and finally, balloons, text and sound effects are added: the completed work ultimately is sent out so that printing negatives can be made directly from over 200 megabytes of computer files. No "physical artwork" is produced. Indeed, the full color digital separations in DIGITAL JUSTICE represent a genuine technological breakthrough.

In serving as a consultant to this project, I have had the luxury of dropping by Pepe's studio and seeing his progress in major leaps; I always walked away amazed and speechless. Imagine a chalk-talk orchestrated by Lucasfilm's Industrial Light and Magic and you'll begin to understand the feeling.

Within the *next* five years, we may have other projects that will make DIGITAL JUSTICE look antique. By that time, the techniques and methods pioneered by Pepe Moreno will have been incorporated invisibly into the mainstream of comic art production, and DIGITAL JUSTICE will inspire dozens of other creators to make their own unique contributions.

The computer employs the same stock in trade as does the comic book: both play to our sense of wonder. DIGITAL JUSTICE marks the next chapter in our development, and a preview of what is to come.

BATMAN: DIGITAL JUSTICE
ISBN I 85266 274 2

Published by Titan Books Ltd
58 St. Giles High Street
London WC2H 8LH

First British edition, April 1990.
10 9 8 7 6 5 4 3 2 1

DIGITAL JUSTICE

1 ▶

BATMAN

Gotham Megatropolis.
Sometime into the next century.

Welcome to Future Land! Take a ride on the Progress Express.

Around you is an apparently perfect world—but this is a "Make-believe World" with vengeance, a world with no soul and a heart that beats in binary code. One or zero—God or the Void.

A complex and wired world dominated by a tyrant code, a computer virus from long ago that has become the world's first Digital Dictator.

The only hope is a myth from the past, from a time of legend and superstition, long before the virus plagues.

A new kind of hero, a program of "clean" code and pure memory, a program written by a legendary Crime Fighter...

A Digital Hero, one that can restore digital truth and...

Digital Justice.

BLEEP!

BLEEP!

BLEEEEEEP

OKAY, MAN--TAKE THE "Q"S--TEST 'EM ON YOUR TWO 'BOYS.' *MIND* STEROIDS'D BE A CHANGE FOR *THEM!*

THEY'VE MADE THE EXCHANGE! LET'S GET THIS ANALYSIS CANNED! IF IT CHECKS, WE MOVE IN--BY THE NUMBERS...

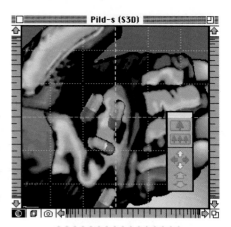

ANALYSIS IN PROGRESS...SERIAL #3296HW172.

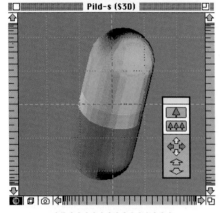

PROBABLE ORIGIN: PANAMA CITY, ADEEDAS PHARM...RED FLAG ALERT!

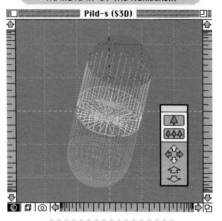

PER REFERENCE JUDICIAL COMP CODE C19885--SALE OR USE OF SUBSTANCE ILLEGAL...

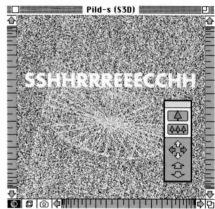

ALL RIGHT! WE GOT THE HARDCOPY.

WHAT THE HELL! IT'S BREAKING UP--

SOMETHING'S CRASHED! ALL UNITS, MOVE IN **NOW!** LENA! WHAT THE HELL IS GOING ON?! LENA?!

REFERENCE MUNICIPAL CODE AA98868, ALL SUBJECTS IN CONTROLLED AREA PREPARE FOR SEARCH AND IDENTIFICATION PROCEDURE...

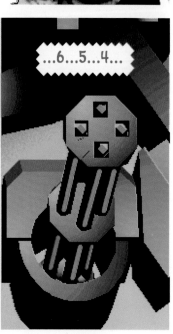

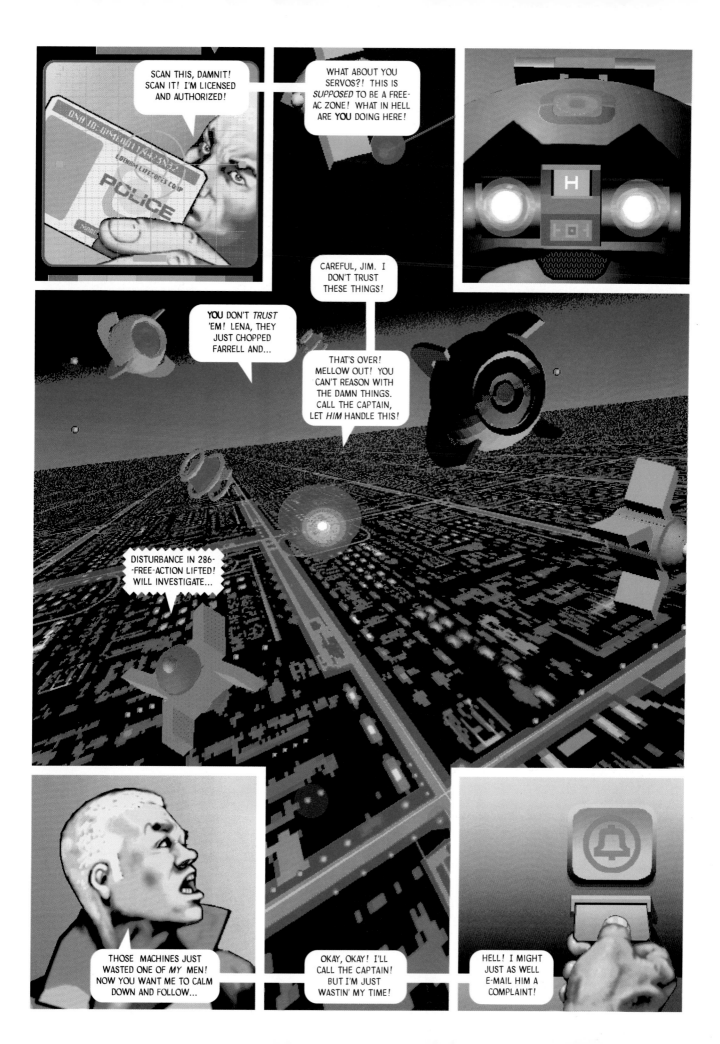

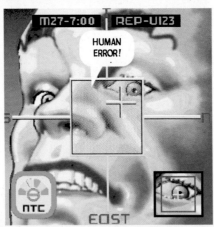

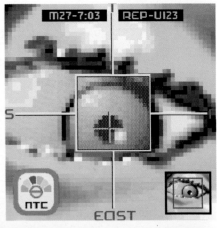

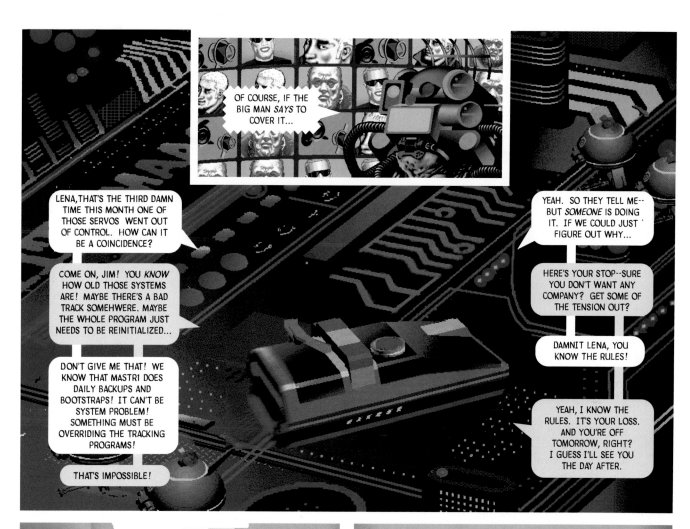

OF COURSE, IF THE BIG MAN *SAYS* TO COVER IT...

LENA, THAT'S THE THIRD DAMN TIME THIS MONTH ONE OF THOSE SERVOS WENT OUT OF CONTROL. HOW CAN IT BE A COINCIDENCE?

COME ON, JIM! YOU *KNOW* HOW OLD THOSE SYSTEMS ARE! MAYBE THERE'S A BAD TRACK SOMEHWERE. MAYBE THE WHOLE PROGRAM JUST NEEDS TO BE REINITIALIZED...

DON'T GIVE ME THAT! WE KNOW THAT MASTRI DOES DAILY BACKUPS AND BOOTSTRAPS! IT CAN'T BE SYSTEM PROBLEM! SOMETHING MUST BE OVERRIDING THE TRACKING PROGRAMS!

THAT'S IMPOSSIBLE!

YEAH. SO THEY TELL ME-- BUT *SOMEONE* IS DOING IT. IF WE COULD JUST FIGURE OUT WHY...

HERE'S YOUR STOP--SURE YOU DON'T WANT ANY COMPANY? GET SOME OF THE TENSION OUT?

DAMNIT LENA, YOU KNOW THE RULES!

YEAH, I KNOW THE RULES. IT'S YOUR LOSS. AND YOU'RE OFF TOMORROW, RIGHT? I GUESS I'LL SEE YOU THE DAY AFTER.

BETTER PICK UP SOMETHING TO EAT--

...TAKE ABOUT THIRTY CREDS WORTH--LEAVE A COUPLE STRIPES 'TIL PAYDAY.

ELECTRONIC GROCER

CREDIT CODE 311420

TRANSACTION COMPLETED TWENTY-EIGHT CREDITS TRANSFERRED...

THANK YOU COME AGAIN.

NICE, POLITE PROGRAM. HOW COME THE MASTR AND THE SERVOS DON'T ACT THAT WAY?

GOTTA GET SOME SLEEP, EYES FEEL LIKE THEY'VE BEEN LASER- SCANNED...BATTERIES RUNNIN' DOWN--REALLY NEED THAT DAY OFF...

THOSE MACHINES *NEVER* NEED TIME OFF...MAYBE IF THERE'S A BROWN- OUT--WISHFUL THINKING! THEY'VE GOT THEIR OWN POWER SOURCE...

PLUGGED IN 'ROUND THE CLOCK...

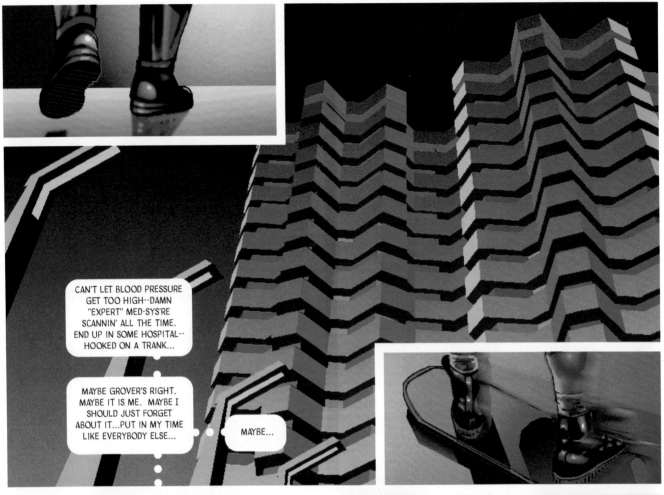

CAN'T LET BLOOD PRESSURE GET TOO HIGH--DAMN "EXPERT" MED-SYS'RE SCANNIN' ALL THE TIME. END UP IN SOME HOSPITAL-- HOOKED ON A TRANK...

MAYBE GROVER'S RIGHT. MAYBE IT IS ME. MAYBE I SHOULD JUST FORGET ABOUT IT...PUT IN MY TIME LIKE EVERYBODY ELSE...

MAYBE...

GANGWAY! EDI-WA! GET OUT OF THE WAY!

HEY! WATCH WHERE...BOBBY? BOB CHANG! SLOW DOWN!

WELL, WELL, LOOK WHO'S HERE!

HEY, PIXEL-PUSS! YOUR ASS IS OURS!

NEO-SURFERS! AREN'T YOU OUT OF YOUR TERRITORY?

WE'VE EXPANDED. NOW, SHOW SOME BRAINS AND GET OUT OF OUR WAY!

I'M TOO TIRED FOR THIS GIGO CRAP! YOU KNOW THE RULES--NO DRAFTS UNLESS THE TURF IS INVADED.

ANY BEACHHEADS I DON'T KNOW ABOUT?

NO "BEACHHEADS"-- JUST A Q-HEAD WHO RIDES ONE OF OUR BOARDS AND TRIES TO TELL *MY* TROOPS WHAT TO DO...

THEN RUNS AND HIDES BEHIND SOME COP!

I DON'T HAVE TO HIDE BEHIND ANYONE, VID-HEAD! I COULD DREZ YOU ANYTIME...

MUTE IT! RIGHT NOW! ONE MORE WORD AND I GO OFFICIAL--ON ALL OF YOU! YOU COPY?

THEN, INSIDE--

THANKS FOR THE HAND BACK THERE, BUT I WAS JUST RUNNIN' 'EM AROUND UNTIL THE *BIG* GUYS DROPPED OUT!

HEY, THERE'S A GATA CONCERT ON CABLE TONIGHT...OR THE GAME ON...

NOT TONIGHT, KID. I'M BEAT. I'LL HAVE THE 'PHONE DISC IT SO WE CAN WATCH IT SOME OTHER TIME--OKAY?

COOL, SERGEANT ROCK! YOU WANNA MAKE SOME EASY COMPANY--I GET IT. SEE YA.

SERGEANT ROCK? WHERE DOES HE GET THAT STUFF?

OKAY, I'M HOME. YOU GOT ANYTHING WORTH MY TIME?

GOOD EVENING, JAMES. I HAVE THREE THOUSAND, ONE HUNDRED NEWS-BYTES ACCUMULATED--ALMOST ONE THOUSAND EIGHT HUNDRED FEATURE YOU.

WOULD YOU LIKE ME TO PLAY THEM?

ARE THERE ANY MESSAGES?

JUST ONE, FROM CAPTAIN GROVER. ANALYSIS INDICATES HIGH LEVELS OF STRESS. SHALL I PLAY IT FOR YOU?

NO THANKS, I *KNOW* WHAT HE WANTS. LET'S SEE THE TEEVEE STUFF.

CERTAINLY:

HERE AT HOME, THE NEO-NEO NAZIS ARE ONCE AGAIN IN THE NEWS.

OBERSTANDARTENFUHRER RICARDO KELLY POINTED OUT THAT IT WAS HIS DUTY TO KEEP THE WORLD SAFE FOR "OLIVE-SKINNED, FAIR-HAIRED 19-TO-28 YEAR-OLDS..."

HE SAID THAT THE "SOCIALLY USELESS" SHOULD BE ELIMINATED--

THIS TIME, WITH *NO* ADD-ONS REPORTED, THE DOA'S *PROVED* THEIR LACK OF INTELLIGENCE, SELF-INFLICTING SEVERAL DEATHS AND SCORES OF INJURIES. GATA HERSELF WAS UNINVOLVED.

MORE AFTER THIS:

ARE THE STREETS SAFER TONIGHT? *WE* THINK SO AND WE'RE PROUD OF WHAT WE SEE! SINCE THE MOD THREE SERVO-ENFORCER UNIT TOOK TO THE STREETS IN 1994, THE CRIME RATE HAS DECREASED BY MORE THAN SEVENTY PERCENT...

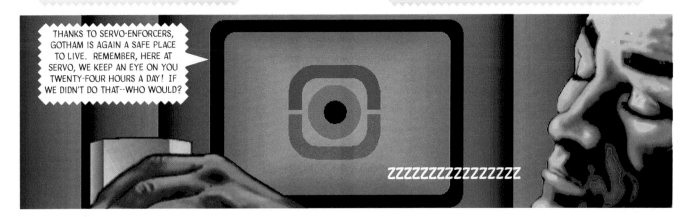

THANKS TO SERVO-ENFORCERS, GOTHAM IS AGAIN A SAFE PLACE TO LIVE. REMEMBER, HERE AT SERVO, WE KEEP AN EYE ON YOU TWENTY-FOUR HOURS A DAY! IF WE DIDN'T DO THAT--WHO WOULD?

ZZZZZZZZZZZZZZZ

AS JIM GORDON DOZES, IN THE HEART OF THE CITY, A WELL-DRESSED COUPLE WORKS ON THEIR OWN BRAND OF 'RELAXATION'...

C'MON BABE, LET'S WALK THROUGH THE PARK. I HAVEN'T BEEN IN HERE SINCE THE 20'S!

WHAT A PERVERSE IDEA! ISN'T IT DANGEROUS IN THERE?

TO SOMEONE LIKE ME? YOU MUST BE KIDDING!

WHO'S GOING TO MESS WITH A NET EXECUTIVE? THE WHOLE SYSTEM'D COME DOWN ON HIM SO FAST...

A NEW DAY DAWNS ON GOTHAM. THE STREETS COME ALIVE AS THE PRIVILEGED FEW SCURRY TO THEIR JOBS. OTHERS, LESS LUCKY, TAKE THEIR TRANKS AND TURN ON THE TEEVEE...

JIM GORDON TRIES TO RELAX--WITHOUT MUCH SUCCESS--OR MUCH HELP...

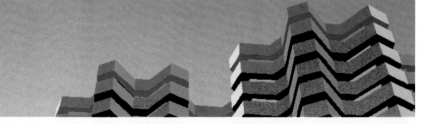

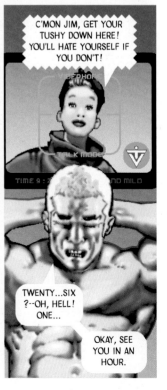

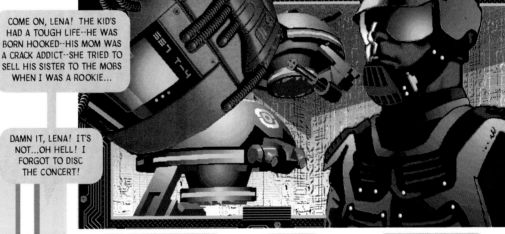

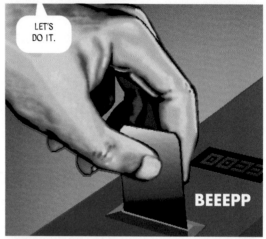

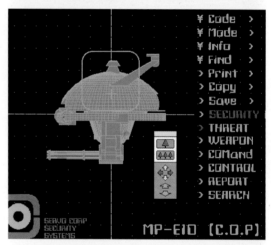

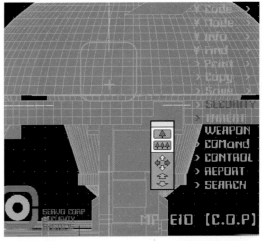

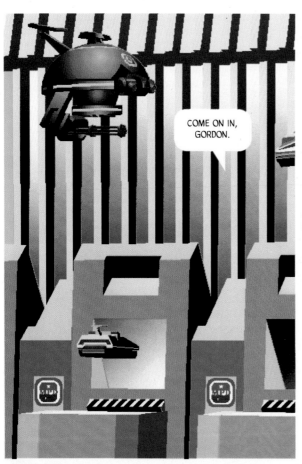

COME ON IN, GORDON.

I HOPE THIS IS IMPORTANT, CAPTAIN. I WAS ON THE BRINK OF...

SHUT THE DOOR.

WHAT THE HELL ARE YOU DOING? MY TERMINAL TELLS ME SOMEBODY'S ILLEGALLY ACCESSING THE MAINFRAME AND I FIND *YOU*! ISN'T THIS YOUR DAY OFF? DIDN'T I TELL YOU TO LET I.A.D. TAKE CARE OF THIS ENFORCER THING?

WAIT A MINUTE! LENA CALLED ME IN AND...

SHUT UP--SERGEANT! THERE'RE EXPERT SYSTEMS WORKING AROUND THE CLOCK ON THIS--THE MALF IS AT *CODE* LEVEL--AND YOU'RE JUST TICKING THEM OFF! THEY'RE THREATENING TO CUT TERMINAL ACCESS AND...

THREATENING YOUR CUSHY JOB? YOUR NICE VIEW?

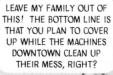

THAT'S ENOUGH! YOU KNOW, *COMMISSIONER* GORDON WAS QUITE A COP--HE GAVE ME MY CHANCE ON THE FORCE. I OWE HIM--AND I CUT YOU SLACK BECAUSE HE WAS YOUR GRANDFATHER, BUT...

LEAVE MY FAMILY OUT OF THIS! THE BOTTOM LINE IS THAT YOU PLAN TO COVER UP WHILE THE MACHINES DOWNTOWN CLEAN UP THEIR MESS, RIGHT?

GIVE IT A REST, GORDON! DROP IT BEFORE THEY KICK YOU AND ME BOTH OUT--AND YOU KNOW THEY WOULD.

TO HELP YOU DO THAT, I'VE GOT A NICE, *QUIET* ASSIGNMENT FOR YOU--STRAIGHT FROM THE MAYOR HERSELF!

YOU RECOGNIZE **GATA**? WELL, THERE'VE BEEN SOME THREATS--AND WE DON'T WANT ANYTHING TO HAPPEN TO A CELEBRITY, NOW, DO WE?

YOU MAKE SURE SHE'S SAFE UNTIL I TELL YOU OTHERWISE-- CLEAR? NOW, GET OUT OF HERE!

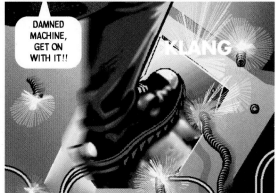

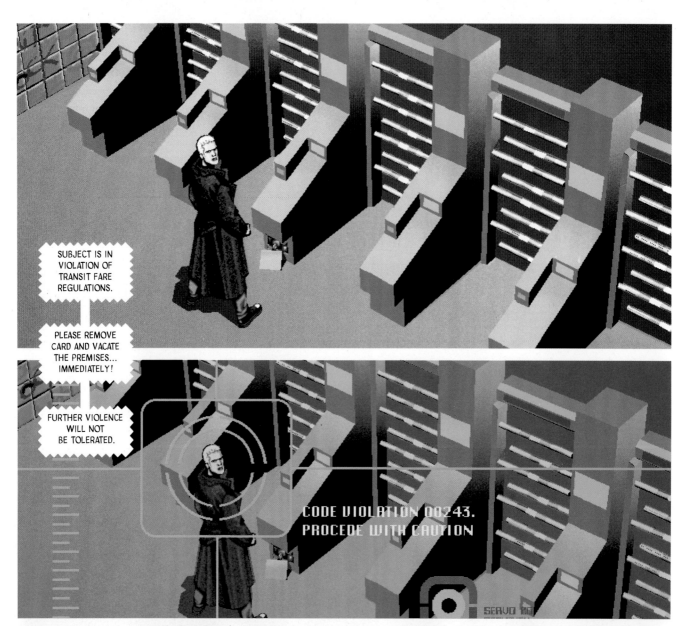

DIGITAL JUSTICE

2 ▶

BATMAN

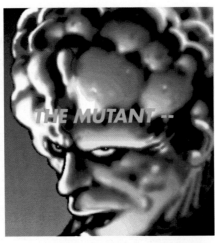

DAMN! CAUGHT WITH MY PANTS DOWN LIKE SOME ROOKIE!

GOT TO SLOW THEM DOWN UNTIL I CAN GET SOME POSITION-- THE LIGHTS!

BLAMM! BLAMM! BLAMM!

THE LIGHTS FLICKER--AND GO OUT. LITTLE MATTER TO KILLERS WITH INFRA-RED SIGHTS...

YOU THINK YOU'RE SCARING ME? I'M GATA! I DON'T SCARE! SHOOT! GO AHEAD! I DARE YOU!

GET DOWN!

DAMN YOU, I SAID GET DOWN!

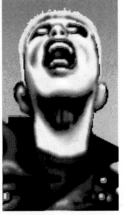

BRRTT!..BRRTT!..BRRTT!..BRRTT!..

DO YOU WANT TO GET KILLED?!

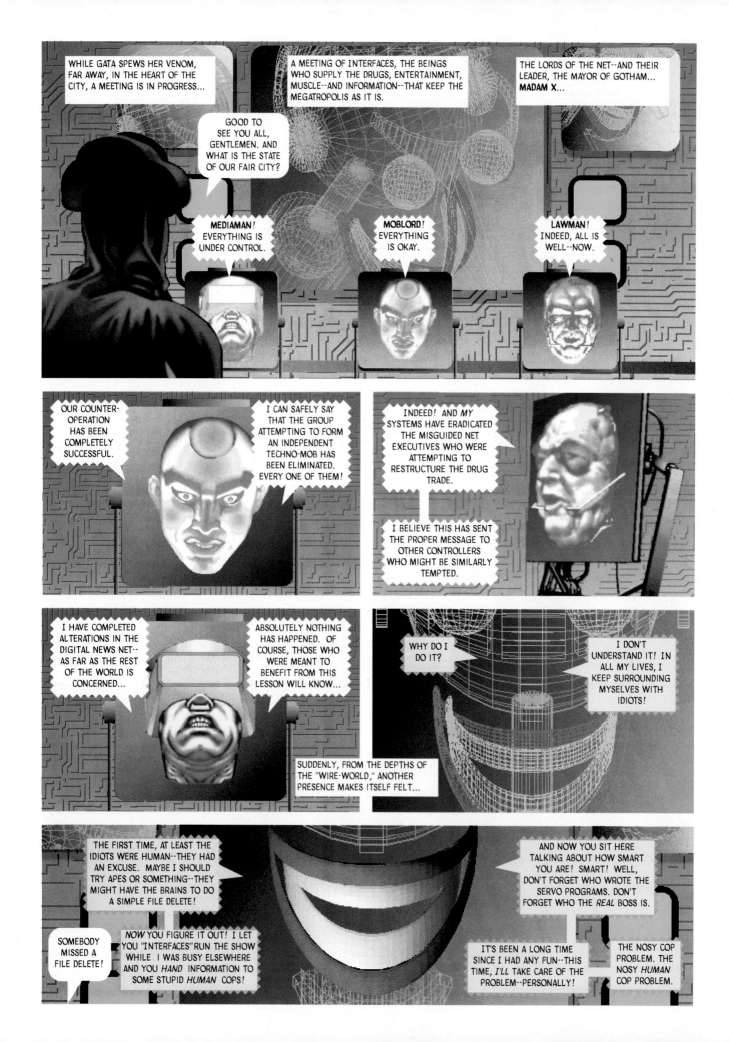

LATER THAT NIGHT AT HIS APARTMENT COMPLEX, JIM GORDON HAS HIS OWN PROBLEMS TO SOLVE-- VERY SERIOUS PROBLEMS...

DAMN! I *KNOW* THAT WAS THE RIGHT ACCESS CODE!

FIRST I GET HOME FROM THAT MESS AT THE CONCERT AND MY 'PHONE TELLS ME I'M SUSPENDED FROM THE FORCE! "CAN'T GET AROUND WITHOUT FULL ACCESS," IT SAYS.

THE CAPTAIN WOULDN'T EVEN TAKE THE TIME TO TALK TO ME IN PERSON!

I'M LOCKED OUT OF MY BANK ACCOUNTS, AND NOW I CAN'T EVEN GET INTO MY OWN TERMINAL!

AND WHERE THE HELL IS LENA! IT'S AFTER ELEVEN! SHE SHOULD HAVE BEEN HERE HOURS AGO!

I NEED SOME ANSWERS AND I CAN'T EVEN REACH THE *KNOW-MAN!* I KNOW HE NEVER GOES OUT, BUT ALL I GET IS HIS ROBOPHONE!

I'VE GOT TO KNOW WHAT THE HELL IS GOING ON--MAYBE I'LL DROP BY...

BEEEPPP!!

THE DOOR! LENA? IT'S ABOUT TIME!

OH, IT'S YOU!

NICE WELCOME, SARGE! OKAY IF I COME UP?

NOT NOW--I'M JUST LEAVING. I'D APPRECIATE IT IF YOU'D KEEP AN EYE OUT FOR LENA, THOUGH.

SAY NO MORE! YOU GOT IT!

NOW, IMAGINE HOW YOU'D FEEL IF THAT PLEASURE WAS SUDDENLY INTERRUPTED...

COME ON, LET ME IN! I KNOW YOU'RE JUST PLAYING YOUR LITTLE "LAX" GAMES IN THERE!

BEEEEEEEPP!!

IMAGINE EVERY PART OF YOUR BODY BEING STROKED, FINGERS TOUCHING IN JUST THE RIGHT PLACES TO MAKE YOU FEEL SO GOOD...

GORDON! I SHOULD HAVE KNOWN! WHAT DO YOU WANT THIS TIME?

I'M COMING UP. I'LL EXPLAIN...

I *KNOW* ABOUT THAT! THE WHOLE UNDERGROUND IS DOWN. DATA BASES HAVE BEEN GETTING WIPED FOR THE PAST 24 HOURS. ALL THE MAINS ARE ACTING CRAZY! BIG BROTHER IS REALLY TICKED OFF ABOUT SOMETHING...

I NEED YOUR HELP. I'M ONTO SOMETHING BIG! BUT MY ACCESS IS SCREWED UP! MY OWN TERMINAL IS ALL BACKED UP...

WHAT DO YOU MEAN, "BIG BROTHER"?

DON'T WORRY ABOUT IT--HE'S CODE-LEVEL STUFF. ANCIENT HISTORY. NOW, WHAT EXACTLY ARE YOU AFTER?

I'M NOT SURE...

TYPICAL!

MY PARTNER FOUND SOME RECORDS OF SECRET TELEPRESENCE MEETINGS--I DON'T HAVE THE HARDCOPY YET, BUT I THOUGHT YOU MIGHT KNOW WHO HAS THAT LEVEL OF AUTHORIZATION...

TELEPRESENCE! YOU'RE OUT OF YOUR DEPTH! ONLY HUMAN INTERFACES *WAY* UP IN THE NET HAVE THAT KIND OF POWER! TOO HIGH FOR A COP.

WE KNOW OF A "SECRET SOCIETY" UP THERE, BUT WE DON'T INTERFERE WITH THEM--TOO CLOSE TO THE SOURCE. I CAN'T HELP YOU WITH THAT!

IF YOU GET A COPY OF THESE MEETINGS, I MIGHT BE ABLE TO GIVE YOU SOMETHING--OFFLINE, OF COURSE--I WOULDN'T WANT **THAT** SORT OF HEAT ON THE UNDERGROUND.

JUST BE CAREFUL-- *REAL* CAREFUL.

SURE HOPE LENA'S OKAY. WE'RE GONNA NEED THAT DISC OF HERS TO GET TO THIS *SECRET SOCIETY*...THING...

"BIG BROTHER"-- I WONDER WHAT HE MEANT BY THAT...

WHAT THE HELL! THIS THING'S FALLING!

THAT DAMN SMILE AGAIN! IT'S AS IF SOMEONE IS WATCHING! CONTROLLING ALL THIS!

LAUGHING AT ME...

ONLY ONE THING LEFT TO DO...

SMASH!!

...I HOPE IT WORKS!

GORDON'S GAMBLE DOES WORK. CUT OFF FROM THE OUTSIDE COMMAND, THE ELEVATOR'S OLD CPU AUTOMATICALLY REACTS TO THE SITUATION AT HAND, AND...

THE EMERGENCY BRAKES ARE CATCHING! IT'S SLOWING DOWN!

IT STOPPED. THANK GOD!

BUT THIS WAS NO ACCIDENT! SOMEBODY'S AFTER ME!

AND IF THEY'RE AFTER ME--THAT MEANS LENA'S DISC MUST REALLY BE HOT! I'VE GOT TO FIND HER!

FAST!

BUT JIM GORDON KNOWS *HE* IS SANE. IF HE WEREN'T, THIS WOULDN'T BE REAL-- AND HE WOULDN'T HURT SO MUCH...

LENA--GONE. I'M ALONE. REALLY ALONE.

MY FAULT! I ALWAYS HAD TO BE A COP, FOLLOW THE RULES!

NEVER DARED TO BEND THEM, EVEN A LITTLE--EVEN WHEN IT WOULD HAVE BEEN SO GOOD, SO RIGHT...

IF I HAD, MAYBE SHE'D BE ALIVE...

JIM GORDON WALKS AIMLESSLY, IN SHOCK. HE STRUGGLES TO LESSEN HIS PAIN--AND FAILS...

I'VE GOT TO MAKE THEM PAY! THERE'S NOBODY ELSE TO DO IT! NOBODY WHO CARES! BUT HOW?

I NEED HELP! BIG HELP! AND I'VE FORGOTTEN HOW...

TO PRAY!

AND THEN, APPARENTLY BY CHANCE, HIS FOOT FALLS IN A VERY SPECIAL SPOT...

??

BATMAN! YEAH, THAT WAS IT!

JUSTICE, HUH! I NEED SOME OF THAT. CAN'T REMEMBER THE LAST TIME I HEARD THE WORD!

AS A WEARY JIM GORDON RETURNS TO AN APARTMENT WHICH IS NOT QUITE AS HE LEFT IT...

HELL! SOMEBODY'S BEEN HERE! I WONDER WHAT THEY WERE LOOKING FOR?

THE DISC! THEY MUST BE LOOKING FOR LENA'S DISC! WHAT A MESS...

WHAT'S THAT?

GRANDPA'S STUFF-- NEWSPAPER CLIPPINGS. I FORGOT THIS STUFF WAS AROUND LOOK AT THIS!

BATMAN AGAIN!

HE *DID* GET THINGS DONE! I WISH I COULD...NO, WITH MY CARD THEY'D NAIL ME IN A SECOND!

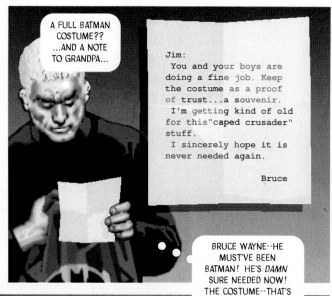

HERE'S THE MONEY! PLEASE DON'T HURT ME! PLEASE...

THANKS FOR THE GREEN! WE'LL JUST HELP OURSELVES TO SOME CHIPS ON THE WAY OUT!

SEVERAL HOURS LATER, DEEP IN THE MEGATROPOLIS, IT'S BUSINESS AS USUAL...

PUT IT BACK, PUNK! ALL OF IT!

HEY MAN, WHO ARE YOU SUPPOSED TO BE?

I AM THE BATMAN!! I OWN THE STREETS NOW. REMEMBER THAT-- AND TELL THE REST OF *YOUR* FRIENDS..

LATER, AS TWO OF THE MOBLORD'S MEN BRING THEIR LATEST LOAD OF GOODS INTO THE CITY...

THIS IS A PAIN, MAN! MOVIN' THIS JUNK IN A TRUCK-- I COULD BE DRIVIN' LEGIT AND...

...MAKIN' THE SAME KIND OF MONEY. WHAT IF WE WERE TO JUST SORT OF TAKE THIS AND...

DEFY-TECH

THUMP!!

FORGET IT! REMEMBER WHAT HAPPENED TO VERZYL WHEN HE TRIED...?

WHAT WAS THAT?!

ONE TRUCKLOAD OF DEATH INTO THE RIVER DOESN'T MEAN MUCH TO THE DRUGLORD--BUT IT IS A START...

A START FOR A MAN WHO KNOWS THAT HE MUST KEEP THE PRESSURE ON. KNOWS THAT HE MUST DISRUPT THE FLOW OF MONEY--

HE HAS ONE ADVANTAGE--LIKE ALL COPS, HE *KNOWS* WHERE THE CRIME IS. NOW, WITHOUT THE FETTERS OF CORRUPT RULES HIDING WITHIN A NEW IDENTITY--

HE CAN DO SOMETHING ABOUT IT.

TRY SOME OF THIS STUFF, MAN!

YEAH, TAKE A FREE SNORT!

I DON'T THINK HE'LL HAVE ANY!

?

WHO DO YOU THINK YOU ARE, MAN! THIS IS OUR TURF!

OH YEAH! WE'LL SEE ABOUT THAT! WE GOT LAWS, MAN--WE GOT RULES! NO JOKER IN A FUNNY COSTUME...

WRONG! IT'S *MINE!*

I'M THE BATMAN!

I DON'T FIGHT BY THE RULES, PUNK--I *MAKE* THEM! THIS IS *MY* CITY NOW!

TIME

IS HE BACK?

ELECTRONIC

MEANWHILE, ON ANOTHER CHANNEL, MILLIONS OF YOUNGER VIEWERS WATCH GATA'S LATEST HYPERVIDEO.

WE INTERRUPT THIS PROGRAM FOR A SPECIAL BULLETIN.

BATMAN!

BATMAN!

BATMAN!

THAT'S ALL I SEE! NOW HE'S CUTTING INTO MY CONCERT COVERAGE! DON'T WE HAVE A CONTRACT OR SOMETHING...

THEY CAN BREAK IN WITH THE NEWS ANYTIME...

GATA MAKES NEWS! WE'RE GOING TO USE THIS BATMAN MANIA! YOU--FIND OUT EVERYTHING ABOUT THIS BATMAN! WHO HE IS, WHO HIS FRIENDS ARE...

WHO HIS ENEMIES ARE-- YEAH, I LIKE THAT! I WANT TO KNOW ALL ABOUT HIS ENEMIES! NOW, DO IT!

I AM THE MAYOR --AND I FEEL POWERLESS! WHO IS HE?!

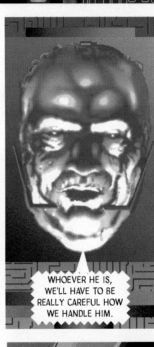

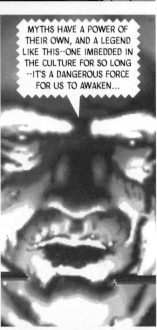

THIS IS MY CITY! I'M THE KING! I'M THE BIGGEST BROTHER OF ALL AND I'M WATCHING! AND WHEN I SEE HIM...

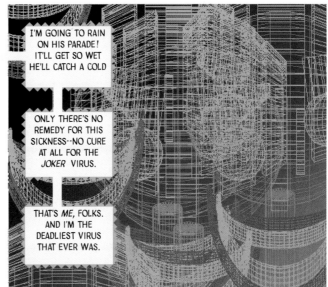

I'M GOING TO RAIN ON HIS PARADE! IT'LL GET SO WET HE'LL CATCH A COLD

ONLY THERE'S NO REMEDY FOR THIS SICKNESS--NO CURE AT ALL FOR THE *JOKER* VIRUS.

THAT'S *ME*, FOLKS. AND I'M THE DEADLIEST VIRUS THAT EVER WAS.

HA! HA! HA! HA! HA! HA! HA! HA! HA! HA! HA! HA!HA! HA! HA!

AND ON THE OUTSKIRTS OF THE CITY--

RELAYS TRIP, CIRCUITS CLOSE, AND POWER GOES ON FOR THE FIRST TIME IN DECADES...

MASTER BRUCE? IS IT TIME?

YES, ALFRED. AT LONG LAST, IT IS TIME!

DIGITAL JUSTICE

3

BATMAN

AS THE MEDIA GOES ABOUT ITS BUSINESS, JIM GORDON MAKES HIS WAY TO GOTHAM NECROPOLIS, WAY STATION FOR THE NEWLY DEPARTED...

IT'S HIS LAST CHANCE TO PAY HIS RESPECTS TO SOMEONE HE LOVED-- AND NEVER REALLY KNEW AT ALL...

...SUMMA CUM LAUDE. AS A MEMBER OF THE DETECTIVE SQUAD, MS. SCHWARTZ ADDED FURTHER LUSTER TO...

WHAT A LOAD OF CRAP!

WHAT DID YOU EXPECT, THE TRUTH?

WHAT ARE YOU DOING HERE, CAPTAIN?

LOOKING FOR YOU. YOU'RE LUCKY ALL THE BIG BOYS ARE LOOKING FOR THAT BATFREAK--THAT'S WHY YOU'RE STILL ALIVE.

I'D LIKE TO KEEP YOU THAT WAY--THIS MIGHT HELP.

I PULLED IT OFF LENA'S BODY BEFORE THE NET GOT TO IT. I FIGURE IT'S WHAT THEY KILLED HER FOR.

I WAS A GOOD COP, ONCE-- I *CARED* ABOUT THINGS-- SOMETIMES I STILL DO. LENA WAS SPECIAL--MAKE SURE *SOMEBODY* PAYS FOR KILLING HER!

MAKE SURE THEY PAY BIG!

LATER, AS GORDON AND THE KNOW-MAN CAREFULLY REVIEW THE DISC ...

THESE OLD CODES... WHAT ARE THEY?

ORIGINAL INTERFACES-- ALL THESE MEETINGS TOOK PLACE AT THE MAYOR'S OFFICE--THESE GUYS ARE HIGHER UP THAN I THOUGHT...

YOU'RE GOING TO NEED HELP ON THIS ONE--MAYBE THAT *CAPED CRUSADER* GUY. KNOW WHERE TO FIND HIM?

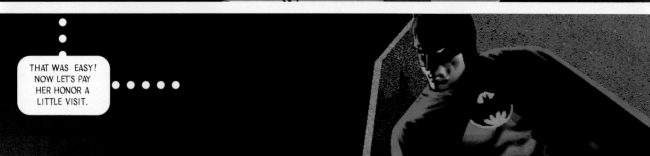

IT HAS BEEN WAITING FOR THIS MOMENT. ITS ORDERS ARE PRE-SET.

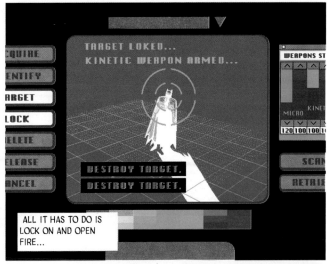

ALL IT HAS TO DO IS LOCK ON AND OPEN FIRE...

GOT...

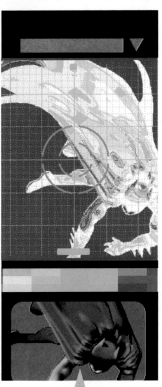

TO...

KEEP...

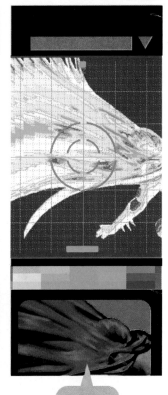

MOVING...

CAN'T DO THIS MUCH LONGER-- GOT TO FIND SOMETHING ELSE...

THIS OLD BELT IS FULL OF STUFF-- MAYBE SOMETHING IN HERE STILL WORKS...

GORDON ACTIVATES EVERY DEVICE IN BATMAN'S "BAG OF TRICKS"--AND HE GETS LUCKY...

ONE OF THE CANISTERS CONTAINS *MAGNETIC SMOKE.* OLD TECH, BUT GOOD ENOUGH TO SCRAMBLE A TARGET LOCK.

A PROCEDURE BEGINS TO DETERMINE THE IDENTITY OF THIS "LEGEND" AND SATISFY THE CURIOSITY OF THE MASTER...

...PROVE THAT THE 'BATMAN' IS MERELY HUMAN AND PUT AND END TO THE NUISANCE...

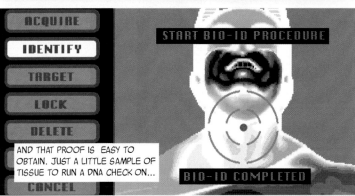

ACQUIRE

IDENTIFY

TARGET

LOCK

DELETE

CANCEL

START BIO-ID PROCEDURE

BIO-ID COMPLETED

AND THAT PROOF IS EASY TO OBTAIN. JUST A LITTLE SAMPLE OF TISSUE TO RUN A DNA CHECK ON...

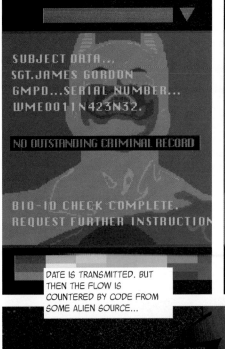

SUBJECT DATA...
SGT.JAMES GORDON
GMPD...SERIAL NUMBER...
WME0011N423N32.

NO OUTSTANDING CRIMINAL RECORD

BIO-ID CHECK COMPLETE.
REQUEST FURTHER INSTRUCTION

DATE IS TRANSMITTED. BUT THEN THE FLOW IS COUNTERED BY CODE FROM SOME ALIEN SOURCE...

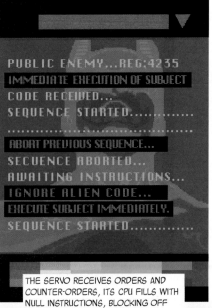

PUBLIC ENEMY...REG:4235
IMMEDIATE EXECUTION OF SUBJECT
CODE RECEIVED...
SEQUENCE STARTED..............
....
ABORT PREVIOUS SEQUENCE...
SECUENCE ABORTED...
AWAITING INSTRUCTIONS...
IGNORE ALIEN CODE...
EXECUTE SUBJECT IMMEDIATELY.
SEQUENCE STARTED.............

THE SERVO RECEIVES ORDERS AND COUNTER-ORDERS, ITS CPU FILLS WITH NULL INSTRUCTIONS, BLOCKING OFF MORE AND MORE STORAGE, UNTIL...

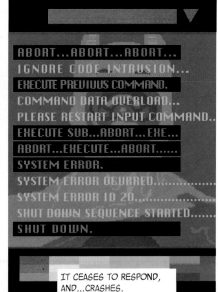

ABORT...ABORT...ABORT...
IGNORE CODE INTRUSION...
EXECUTE PREVIUUS COMMAND.
COMMAND DATA OVERLOAD...
PLEASE RESTART INPUT COMMAND...
EXECUTE SUB...ABORT...EXE...
ABORT...EXECUTE...ABORT......
SYSTEM ERROR.
SYSTEM ERROR OCURRED....
SYSTEM ERROR ID 20.............
SHUT DOWN SEQUENCE STARTED......
SHUT DOWN.

IT CEASES TO RESPOND, AND...CRASHES.

THE BATMAN ONCE AGAIN IS DROPPED TO THE HARD FLOOR...

WHERE HE SLOWLY REGAINS CONSCIOUSNESS. HE IS ALIVE--AND HE HURTS...

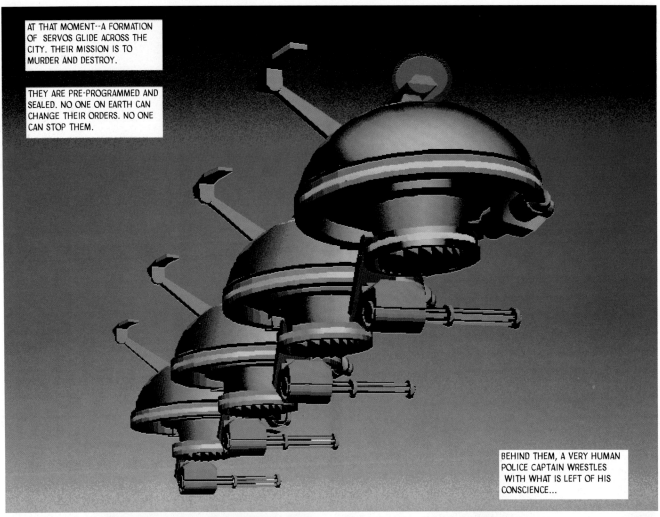

AT THAT MOMENT--A FORMATION OF SERVOS GLIDE ACROSS THE CITY. THEIR MISSION IS TO MURDER AND DESTROY.

THEY ARE PRE-PROGRAMMED AND SEALED. NO ONE ON EARTH CAN CHANGE THEIR ORDERS. NO ONE CAN STOP THEM.

BEHIND THEM, A VERY HUMAN POLICE CAPTAIN WRESTLES WITH WHAT IS LEFT OF HIS CONSCIENCE...

IT'S MY FAULT LENA DIED--MY FAULT.

I CAN'T LET GORDON DIE, TOO! I'VE GOT TO WARN HIM.

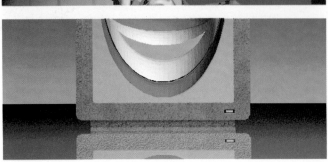

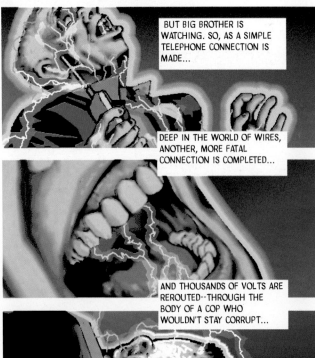

BUT BIG BROTHER IS WATCHING. SO, AS A SIMPLE TELEPHONE CONNECTION IS MADE...

DEEP IN THE WORLD OF WIRES, ANOTHER, MORE FATAL CONNECTION IS COMPLETED...

AND THOUSANDS OF VOLTS ARE REROUTED--THROUGH THE BODY OF A COP WHO WOULDN'T STAY CORRUPT...

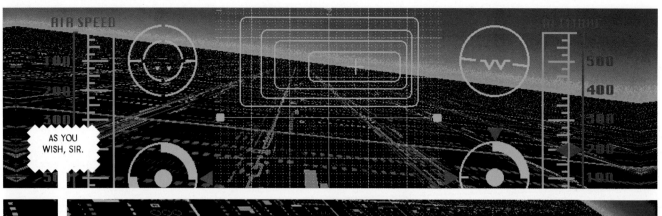

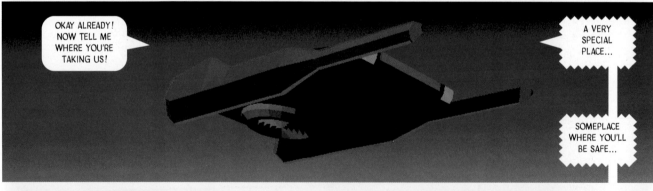

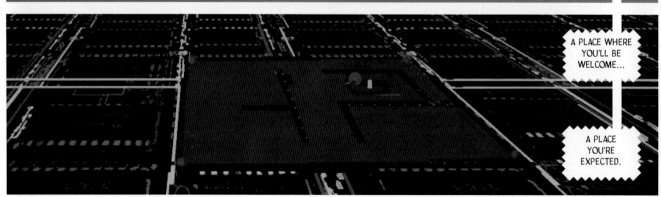

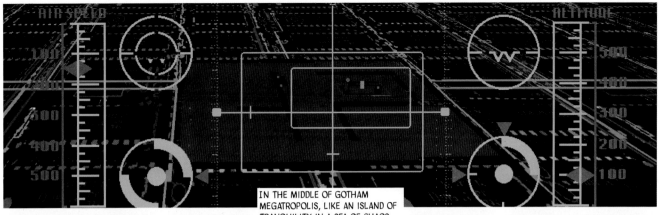

IN THE MIDDLE OF GOTHAM MEGATROPOLIS, LIKE AN ISLAND OF TRANQUILITY IN A SEA OF CHAOS, STANDS WAYNE MANOR...

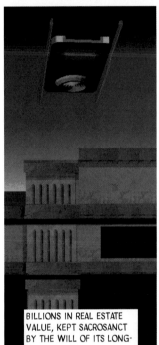

BILLIONS IN REAL ESTATE VALUE, KEPT SACROSANCT BY THE WILL OF ITS LONG-DEAD OWNER...

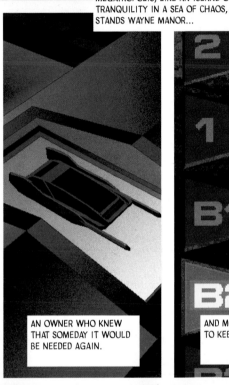

AN OWNER WHO KNEW THAT SOMEDAY IT WOULD BE NEEDED AGAIN.

KLING!!

AND MADE EVERY EFFORT TO KEEP IT READY...

GOOD DAY, GENTLEMEN. SMOKING JACKET?

DON'T MIND ALFRED, HE'S NOT QUITE FULLY FUNCTIONAL.

LET ME BE THE FIRST TO WELCOME YOU TO THE BATCAVE!

OKAY, I ADMIT IT. I'M IMPRESSED.

THE BATCAVE. AND WE'RE STANDING IN IT! WOW!

I'M GLAD THE MANTLE HAS BEEN TAKEN UP BY SOMEONE LIKE YOU--PARTICULARLY GLAD THAT YOUR GRANDFATHER'S GENES BRED TRUE.

MY GRANDFATHER?

INDEED, HE WAS THE CREATOR'S BEST FRIEND.

THE CREATOR?

BRUCE WAYNE--THE *ORIGINAL* BATMAN. YOU'VE BEEN WEARING HIS COSTUME--I'VE BEEN WATCHING YOU IN ACTION--AND TRYING TO KEEP YOU SAFE.

YEAH--OKAY--YOU'RE THE ONE WHO STOPPED THAT SERVO IN THE MAYOR'S OFFICE?

THAT WAS EASY. I WAS PROGRAMMED TO HANDLE JUST THAT SORT OF PROBLEM. OUR MAJOR TASK IS NOT THAT SIMPLE, UNFORTUNATELY...

MAJOR TASK?

I'LL EXPLAIN ALL OF IT IN A MOMENT--FIRST, LET ME PLAY SOME OLD NEWS CLIPS FOR YOU. THEY'LL CLARIFY THINGS, HELP PREPARE YOU FOR WHAT IS YET TO COME...

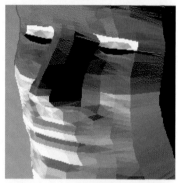

BILLIONAIRE BRUCE WAYNE MADE A RARE PUBLIC APPEARANCE TODAY AT THE UNVEILING OF GOTHAM'S TRIBUTE TO BATMAN.

THE HEROIC STATUE, THE WORK OF NOTED SCULPTOR VICTOR DE LA FUENTES, STANDS AT THE GEOGRAPHIC CENTER OF GOTHAM CITY--DEEP IN GOTHAM PARK...

IT DRAMATIZES THE CONTRIBUTION BATMAN MADE TO JUSTICE IN THIS GREAT CITY. ALSO AT THE DEDICATION WERE...

ARE YOU SURE, BRUCE?

I'M SURE, COMMISSIONER. YOUR BOYS HAVE THINGS WELL IN HAND NOW--AND I'M GETTING A LITTLE OLD TO BE SWINGING AROUND IN THIS CITY. I'LL FIND SOMETHING ELSE TO DO.

AND, OF COURSE, HE DID. MASTER BRUCE REALIZED THAT FUTURE CRIMINAL THREATS WOULD BE FROM ANOTHER WORLD--THE DIGITAL WORLD OF THE COMPUTER...

HE CREATED ME TO HANDLE SUCH THREATS. THE JOB TOOK YEARS-- YEARS DURING WHICH HE LEFT THE PUBLIC'S EYE COMPLETELY.

OF COURSE, THE MEDIA HAD THEIR OWN THEORIES...

...A DIGITAL ALTERATION OF FILE PHOTOS TO GIVE OUR VIEWERS SOME IDEA OF THE POSSIBLE APPEARANCE OF BRUCE WAYNE.. IS THIS THE END RESULT OF GREAT WEALTH? WE'LL LOOK INTO...

WHILE THE CREATOR WORKED, THERE WERE OTHERS ATTEMPTING TO ENTER THE DIGITAL WORLD--FOR LESS NOBLE REASONS. UNTIL FINALLY...

MR. JOKER! IS IT TRUE THAT YOUR COMPUTER VIRUS WAS RESPONSIBLE FOR THE FAILURE OF THE WALL STREET FINANCIAL SYSTEMS?

ME? IT COULDN'T BE ME, THEY JUST FOUND ME NOT GUILTY! ISN'T THIS A GREAT COUNTRY!

AND SO THE JOKER GOES FREE. TED BAXTER ON WALL STREET--BACK TO YOU, DIANE.

THE LAND OF OPPORTUNITY! HA! HA! HA! HA!

NOW THAT HE'S FREE OF HIS PROBLEMS WITH THE LAW, THE JOKER SAYS WE'LL BE SEEING A LOT OF HIM.

HE SAID HE WAS GOING TO TAKE OVER THE TOWN. HE WAS ONLY KIDDING, OF COURSE...

OF COURSE, THE JOKER *WAS* GUILTY--AND AS TIME PASSED, HIS VIRUS PROVED MORE DANGEROUS THAN ANYONE DREAMED. IT SPREAD TO MORE AND MORE SYSTEMS, ACCUMULATING CORE STORAGE--AND POWER. EVENTUALLY, IT BECAME CAPABLE OF MANIPULATING THE POLITICAL AND MEDIA CENTERS OF THIS CITY...

AND QUICKLY GAINED NEAR-TOTAL CONTROL! UNDER THE REIGN OF THIS OUTLAW CODE, TECHNOLOGY HAS BEEN WARPED, FROM THE TOOL OF HUMANITY...TO ITS MASTER! A MASTER WHO HAS STRIVEN TO DELETE LEGEND, FAITH-- AND HOPE--FROM THE HEARTS OF THE PEOPLE.

THAT IS THE MENACE I WAS CONCEIVED TO COMBAT. BUT I KNEW I COULD DO NOTHING WITHOUT HELP-- THE JOKER VIRUS HAS HUMAN AIDES I CANNOT FIGHT. FOR THEM, I NEED...

EXACTLY! I WAS PROGRAMMED TO WAIT FOR SOMEONE WHO COULD EMBODY THE SPIRIT OF THE BATMAN.

US!

YOU'VE ALREADY SEEN THE BATCRAFT AND ITS TREMENDOUS CAPABILITIES, BUT TO BE EFFECTIVE, YOU'LL NEED MORE...

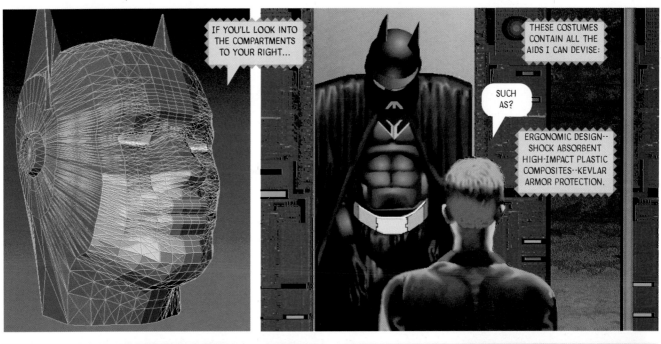

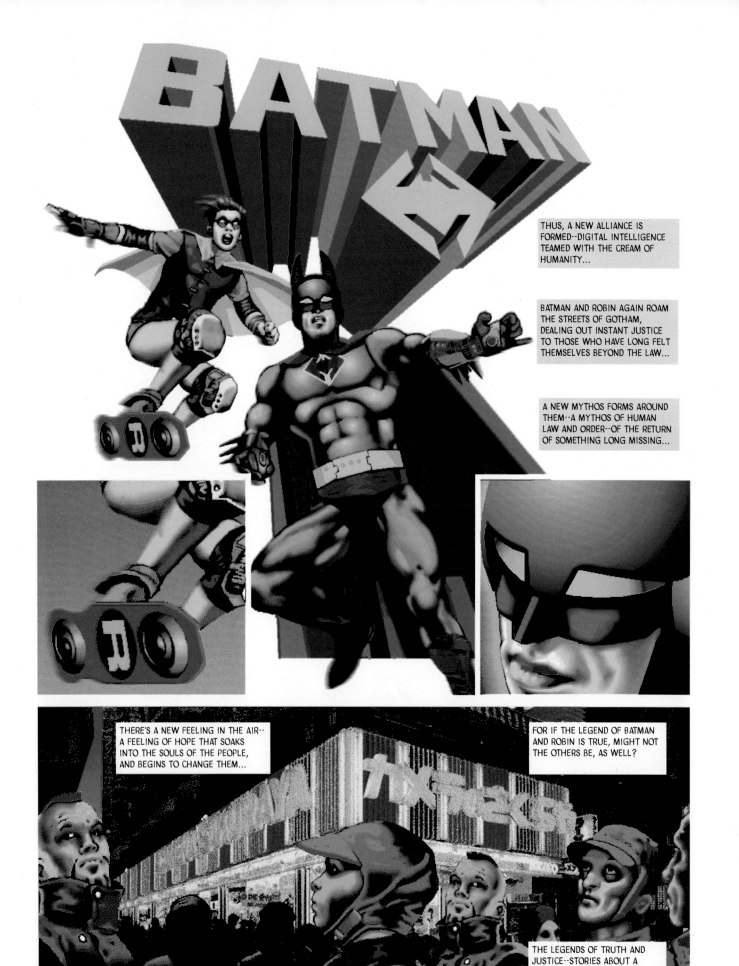

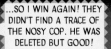

...SO I WIN AGAIN! THEY DIDN'T FIND A TRACE OF THE NOSY COP. HE WAS DELETED BUT GOOD!

AT THE MAYOR'S TOWER--A PLACE WHERE THE VERY CONCEPT OF TRUTH AND JUSTICE HAVE LONG SINCE BEEN DISCARDED...A SMALL CELEBRATION IS TAKING PLACE...

BUT THE PEOPLE! ALL OVER THE CITY THEY'RE TALKING ABOUT THE BATMAN AND THE RETURN OF...

WHO CARES ABOUT THE PEOPLE! I CONTROLLED THEM BEFORE, I'LL CONTROL THEM AGAIN!

MAYBE IT'S TIME FOR ME TO GO PUBLIC! SHOW THEM MY SHINING PERSONALITY! HOW COULD THEY RESIST?

YEAH! THAT'S THE TICKET! THEY WANT LEGENDS! I'LL GIVE THEM THE ULTIMATE--THE NUMBER ONE!--ME! HA! HA! HA! HA!

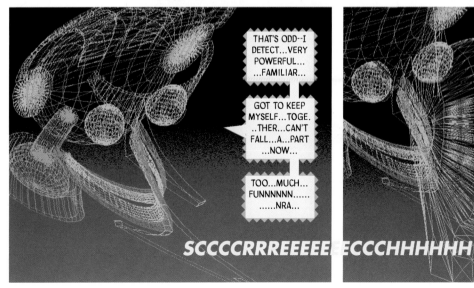

THAT'S ODD--I DETECT...VERY POWERFUL... ...FAMILIAR...

GOT TO KEEP MYSELF...TOGE. ..THER...CAN'T FALL...A...PART ...NOW...

TOO...MUCH... FUNNNNNN...... ......NRA...

SCCCCRRREEEEEEECCCHHHHHH

THE FACE OF EVIL FADES, AND IN ITS PLACE...

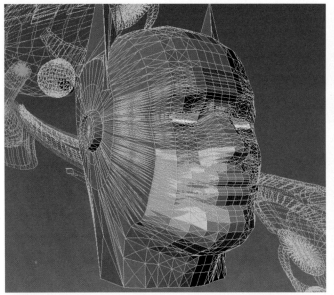
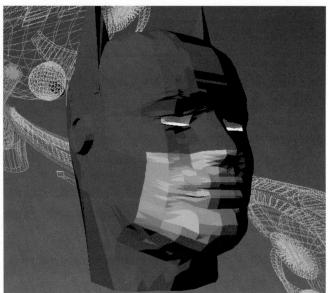

MARK ME WELL. I AM THE END OF ALL THINGS FOR YOU...
THE FACE OF YOUR JUDGE AND JURY...
THE LAST FACE YOU WILL EVER SEE IN THIS WORLD...
THE FACE OF JUSTICE! TRUE JUSTICE!
DIGITAL JUSTICE!

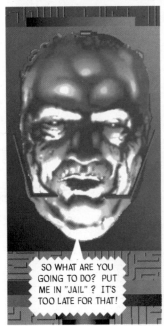

KERASH!!

AND HERE'S THE BIG MAN HIMSELF--THE MOB LORD.

HAVING A TELEPRESENCE MEETING? SWELL! DON'T LET ME--

--INTERRUPT YOU!

MADAM MAYOR...I AM UNDER ATTACK. I'M EXPERIENCING...

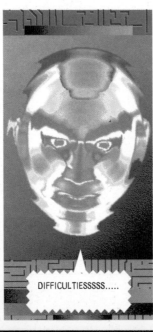

DIFFICULTIESSSSS.....

....

THIS IS INTOLERABLE! ONLY THE MEDIA MAN IS LEFT, AND HE WON'T LAST!

THAT...BATMAN AND HIS SNOTTY COHORT ARE DISMANTLING OUR SOCIETY...

BUT THEY HAVEN'T GOTTEN ME! AND THEY WON'T BE ABLE TO TOUCH THE JOKER...

AND THE MAYOR OF GOTHAM AND THE JOKER CODE ARE THE MOST POWERFUL OF ALL!

MINUTES LATER, HIGH OVER GOTHAM MEGATROPOLIS, A RENDEZVOUS TAKES PLACE.

ONE MADE POSSIBLE BY THE SOPHISTICATION OF THE BATVEHICLE'S SYSTEMS AND THE SKILL OF CHANG...

A RENDEZVOUS THAT MARKS THE BEGINNING OF THE END FOR THE REMNANTS OF THE CRIME CARTEL...

YOU GET HIM?

CAN A CPU ADD ONE AND ZERO? NO SWEAT!

WHERE WE OFF TO NOW? THE MEDIA MAN?

NO. HE'S TOO DEEP IN THE WIRE WORLD FOR US TO TACKLE. HE'S GOT TO BE TAKEN FROM THE INSIDE-- A DIGITAL ATTACK...

AND IF THAT GLOW FROM HIS TOWER IS ANY INDICATION, OUR COMPUTER FRIEND IS ALREADY ON THE JOB!

BELOW, IN A TOWER DOME THAT HAS SUDDENLY BECOME AN ARENA, THE FINAL, FATEFUL CONFRONTATION BEGINS...

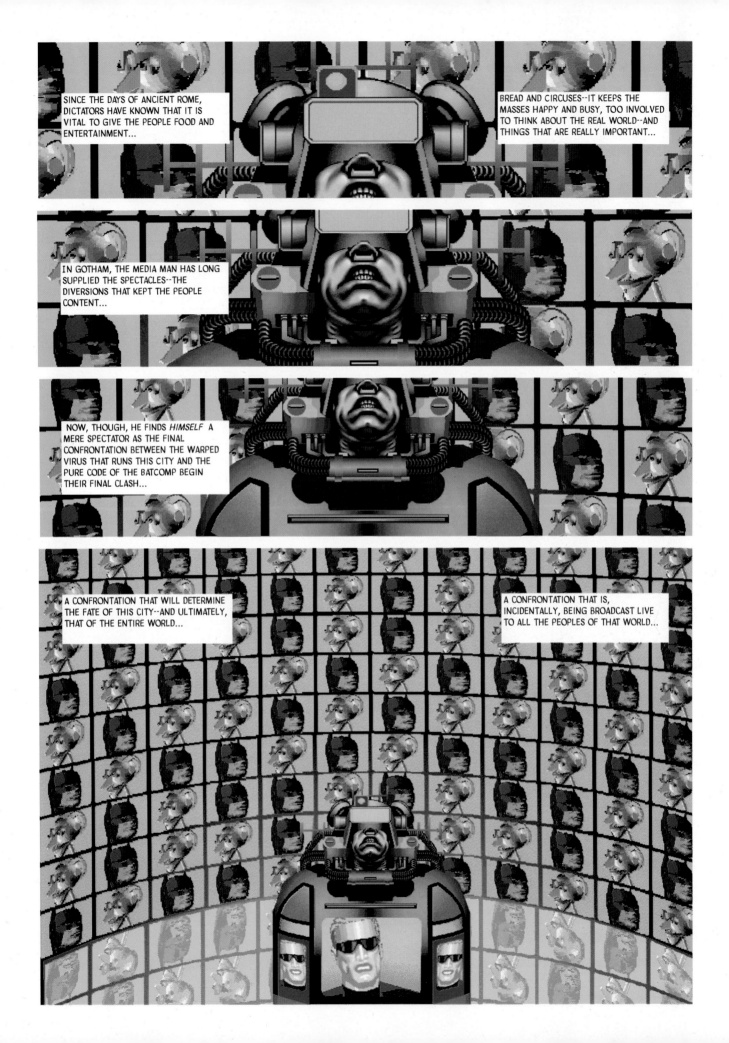

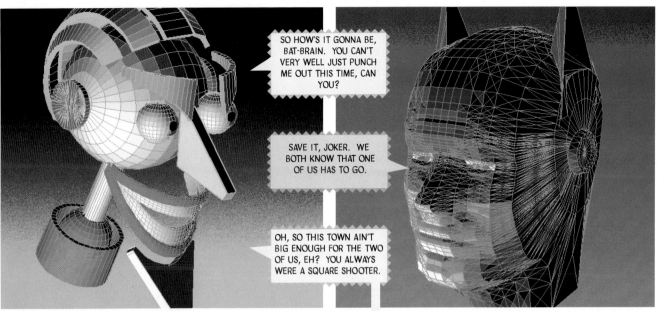

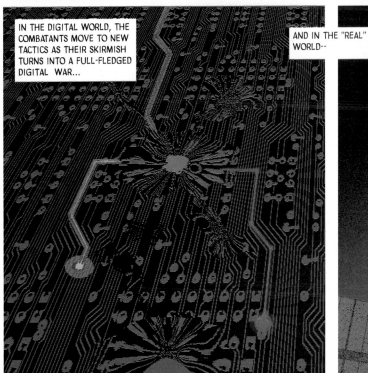

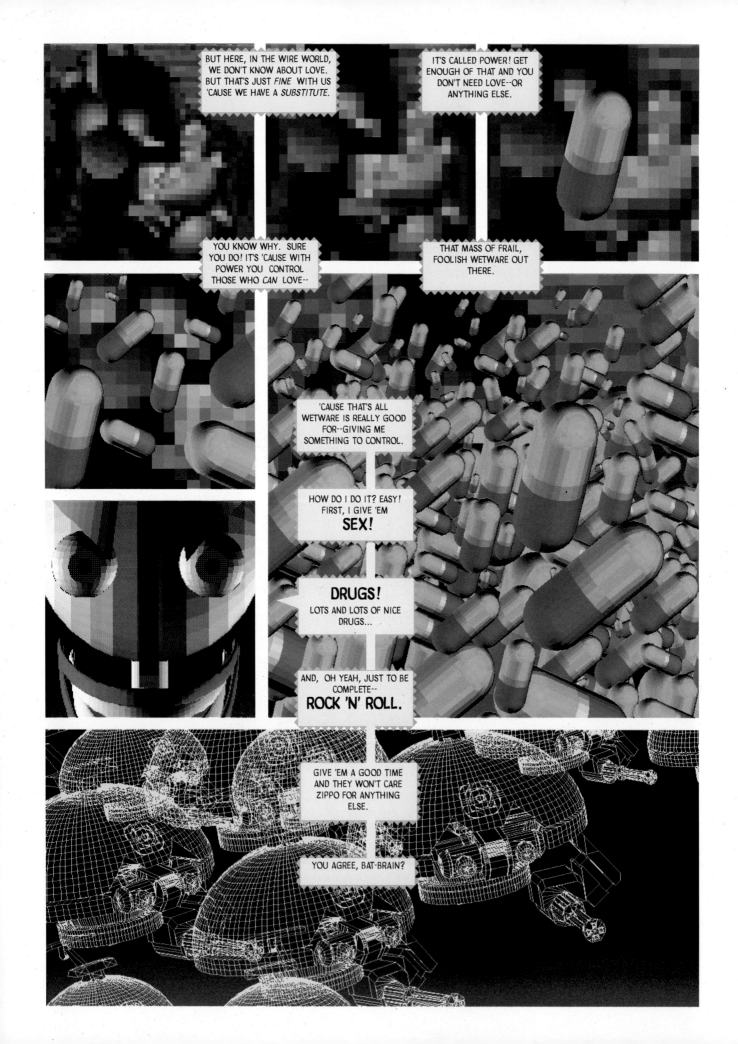

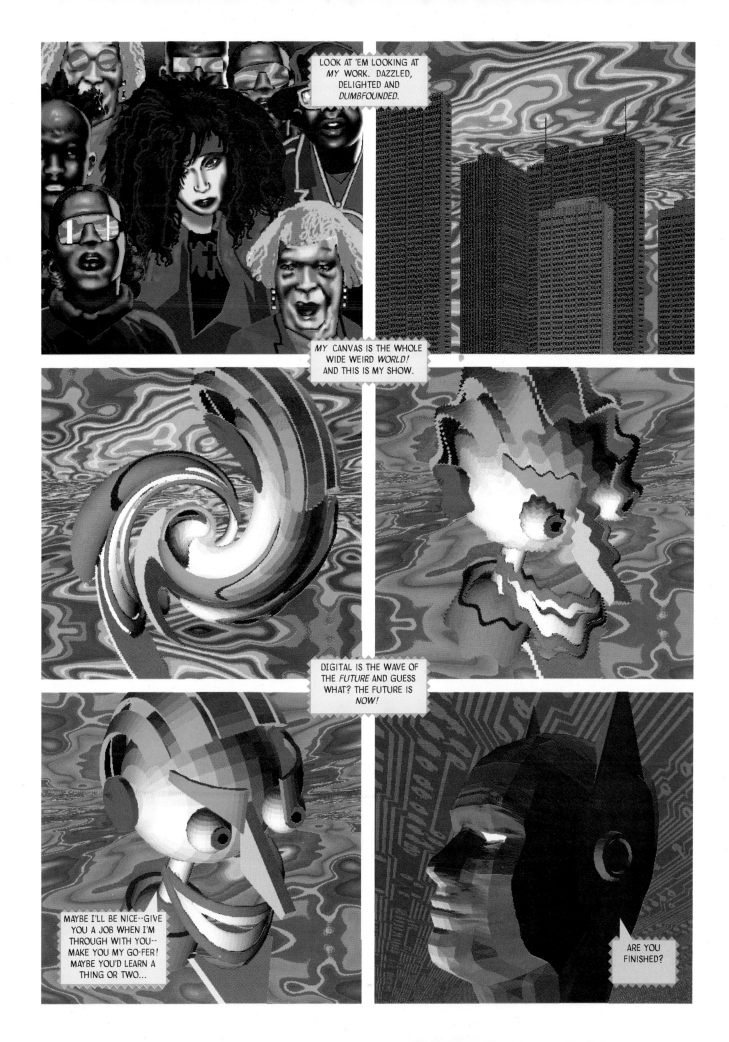

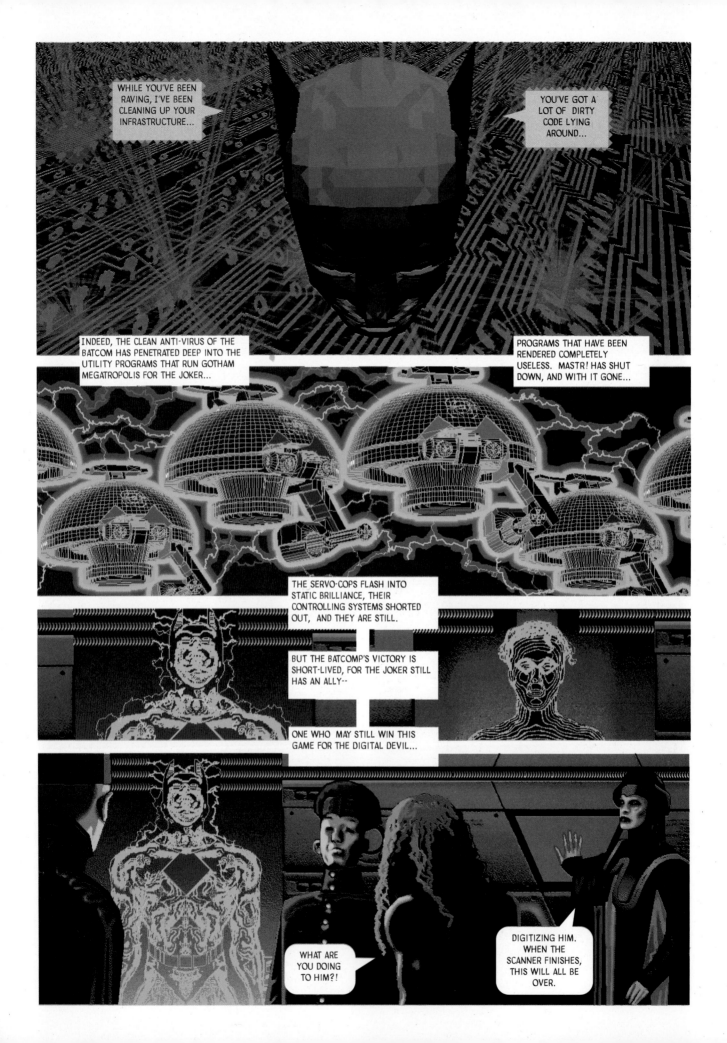

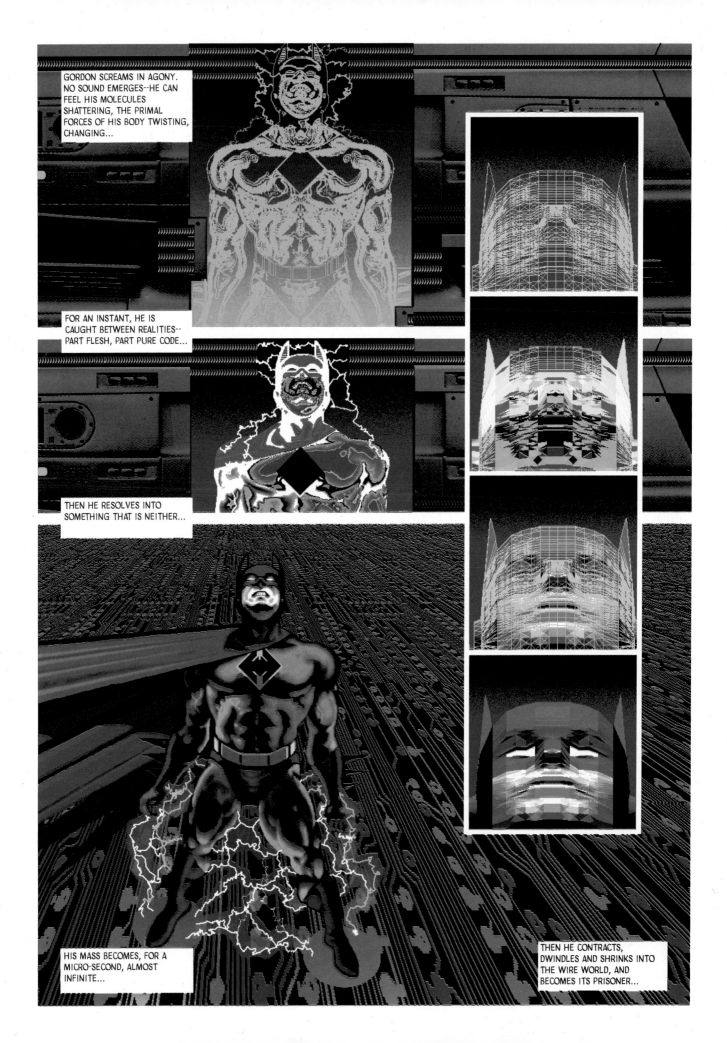

THE COMPUTER TERMINAL STANDS COMPLETELY OUTSIDE THE NET--THE JOKER VIRUS IS TOTALLY UNAWARE OF ITS EXISTENCE...

THE LITTLE ROBOT BOOTS THE SYSTEM, AND THE PURE CODE OF THE BATCOMP LIVES AGAIN...

AT FIRST, IT IS WEAK, WITH SO LITTLE STORAGE THAT IT COULD EASILY BE DELETED--BUT THE VICTORIOUS JOKER IS TOO BUSY CELEBRATING...

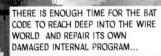

THERE IS ENOUGH TIME FOR THE BAT CODE TO REACH DEEP INTO THE WIRE WORLD AND REPAIR ITS OWN DAMAGED INTERNAL PROGRAM...

POWER SURGES AS BOTH PROGRAMS REACH MAXIMUM CAPACITY. THEY LOCK, FUSE, REACH CRITICAL MASS...

A THERMODIGITAL IMPLOSION OCCURS --THE FIRST IN HISTORY--FORMING A HURRICANE OF CENTRIFUGAL FORCE...

A FORCE THAT DRAGS BOTH PROGRAMS DOWN TOWARD DIGITAL LIMBO... A FORCE MUCH TOO POWERFUL FOR A MERE INTERFACE TO CONTAIN...

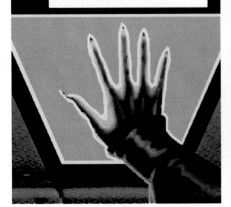

ZZZZZAAAPPPP!!

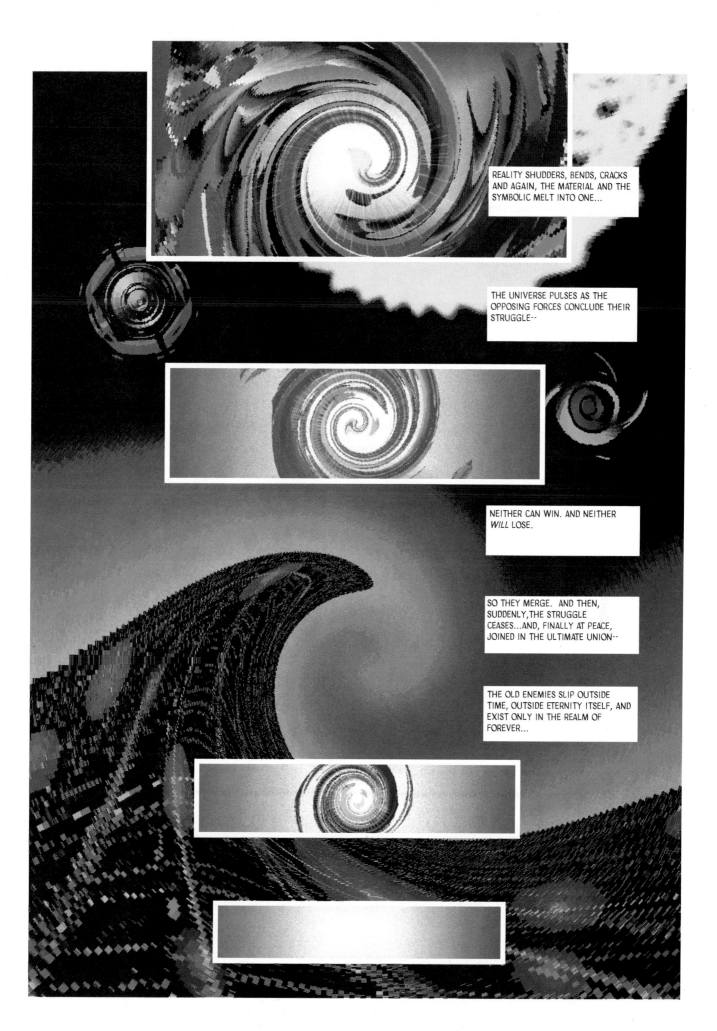

REALITY SHUDDERS, BENDS, CRACKS AND AGAIN, THE MATERIAL AND THE SYMBOLIC MELT INTO ONE...

THE UNIVERSE PULSES AS THE OPPOSING FORCES CONCLUDE THEIR STRUGGLE--

NEITHER CAN WIN. AND NEITHER *WILL* LOSE.

SO THEY MERGE. AND THEN, SUDDENLY,THE STRUGGLE CEASES...AND, FINALLY AT PEACE, JOINED IN THE ULTIMATE UNION--

THE OLD ENEMIES SLIP OUTSIDE TIME, OUTSIDE ETERNITY ITSELF, AND EXIST ONLY IN THE REALM OF FOREVER...

BATCRAFT

Stealth VTOL Multipurpose All Weather Craft

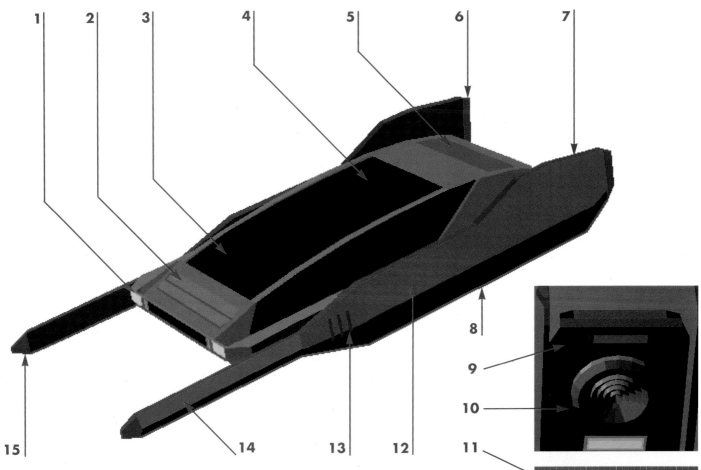

ORIGIN: Wayne Electronics (superconductor division).
ENGINE: Electrical Superconductive VTOL Vector-Thrust turbo-fan with center of gravity nozzle.
DIMENSIONS: Length overall (including LIDAR arm) 6 m ; width 2.25 m ; height (retracted wheels) 1 m.
WEIGHT: Total 500 Kg.
ARMOR: Honeycomb composite high-impact plastics layered with Radar-deflector paint
PERFORMANCE: Unlimited range (maintenance provided); hovering vertical liftoff and landing; maximun horizontal velocity (MHV) Mach 2.1.

ELECTRONICS: Input independent (Artificial Intelligence) fly by wire avionics. Voice recognition command or AI by emergency default ; ECM (Electronic Counter Measures) and CRI (Computer Radar Imaging).
ARMAMENT: The Batcraft is a self-defense oriented vehicle and no aggressive weapons are integrated; however, it will support a wide variety of sophisticated weaponry if required.
COMMUNICATIONS. World wide multimedia network; open line direct communications with the Batcave Batcom computer and the Batsuit helmet

1 HIGH-INTENSITY QUARTZ LIGHTS	**8 ALTITUDE AND PROXIMITY SENSORS**
2 FLUSH ENGINE AIR INTAKE (inlet)	**9 TAKE OFF AND LANDING LIGHTS**
3 HOLOGRAPHIC EMULSION / ELECTRICALLY CHARGED WIND-SHIELD	**10 SVTOL TURBO FAN POWER PLANT**
4 DIGITAL CORE AVIONICS SYSTEM (inside).	**11 HEAD UP HOLOGRAPHIC DISPLAY**
5 HIGH DENSITY BATTERY PACK POWER SOURCE	**12 RADAR-ABSORBENT ARMORED SHIELD**
6 TAIL LIGHTS ECM HOUSING	**13 AIR DATA SENSOR ARRAY**
7 POSITION LIGHTS AND ECM	**14 TWIN MOUNTED SPOT LASER-RADAR (LIDAR)**
	15 ROTATING REACTION CONTROL VALVE (RCV)

BATSUIT
Advanced Technology Body Protection System ATBPS

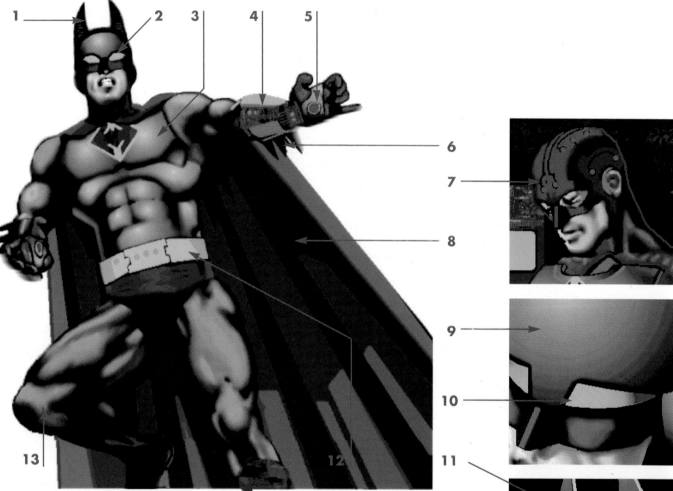

ORIGIN: Wayne Advanced Technology (WAT).

ARMOR: Kevlar layered high-impact plastic composites body armor; ergonomic design; impact dissipator air-impregnated multi-density foams & full body thermo-coolant wear.

WEIGHT: total 2.5 Kg.

PERFORMANCE: High durability materials bounce-back on impact, low maintenance suit.

ARMAMENT: Forearm mounted DEW (Directed Energy Weapon) high-energy chemical laser.

ELECTRONICS: Brain wave interface, helmet Integrated micro-computer; neurological input and output sensor circuitry; logic-thinking accelerator board and 2Gb of storage memory. ECM (Electronic Counter Measures) belt.

COMMUNICATIONS: Long range open communications channel with direct link to the Batcave, Batcom and the Batcraft onboard computer.

---

1 **ULTRASONIC OMNI-DIRECTIONAL LISTENING DEVICE**
2 **KEVLAR HELMET (Bullet proof)**
3 **HIGH-IMPACT PLASTIC COMPOSITE BODY ARMOR**
4 **DEW CHEMICAL LASER MOUNT**
5 **LASER BEAM MUZZLE**
6 **TITANIUM SPIKE SAW**
7 **NEURO CIRCUIT SENSORS**

8 **STEALTH CAPE / RADAR ABSORBENT FABRIC**
9 **IHADS/NVS ELECTRONICS STOWAGE**
10 **EC (Electrically Charged) / MULTI SPECTRUM STEREOSCOPIC LENSES**
11 **GROUND-AIR HOMING RADAR DEVICE**
12 **ECM INTEGRATED CIRCUIT BELT**
13 **THERMO-COOLANT WEAR WITH INTEGRATED ANATOMIC SENSORS**

SERVOCOP
MPE-10 Metro Police Enforcement
(Model 10)

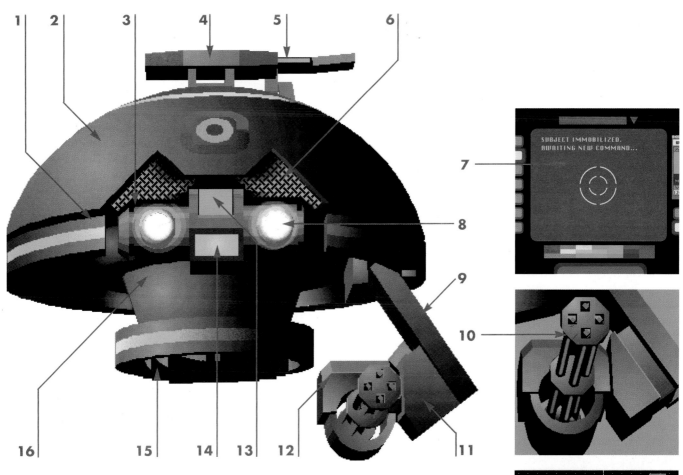

ORIGIN: Servo Corporation.
ENGINE: SVTOL Superconductive Vector-Thrust turbo-fan.
DIMENSIONS: Diameter 4m ; height (retracted gun) 3m; 3.5m aground.
WEIGHT: Empty 2000 Kg; maximum 3000 Kg.
PERFORMANCE: Self-sufficient battery pack; unlimited range (maintenance provided) ; hovering (levitation) ceiling 3000m; maximum speed Mach 1.2.

ARMAMENT: 20mm high-velocity multi-barrel KE (Kinetic Energy) gun. High intensity OMD (Organic Matter Disintegrator) lamps.
ELECTRONICS: RCV (Rotary Reaction Control Valve) Semi-servo unit with limited AI (Artificial Intelligence); ESC (Electronic Self Control); ECM and automatic self-preservation knowledge engine.
COMMUNICATIONS: Central Judiciary Computer link.

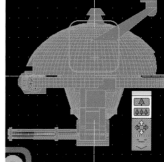

1 MAGNETIC ROTARY RING	**9 RETRACTABLE ARM**
2 NON-METALLIC COMPOUND ARMOR SHIELD	**10 KINETIC ENERGY RAILGUN**
3 ROTARY TADS / MRI SENSOR DROME	**11 MUNITIONS HOUSING (Kinetic Rods)**
4 POLICE WARNING LIGHTS	**12 RAPID FIRE AUTO-FEEDER BRIDGE**
5 0MNI-DIRECTIONAL LIDAR AND RCV	**13 TADS (Target Acquisition Designation Sight)**
6 FORWARD AIR INLET	**14 DIGITAL-MOLECULAR SCANNER**
7 MRI SCREEN DISPLAY (internal)	**15 TURBO FAN NOZZLE**
8 HEAD LAMP STANDARD AND MICROWAVE	**16 SUPERCONDUCTIVE VTOL TURBO-FAN**

DNA ID: WME0011N432N32

GOTHAM LIFECODES CORP

NAME: JAMES GORDON SGT.
DOB: 3-11-2033
RES: 3022 N 900 ST. 808
POB: GTHM

PRO   AKA BATMAN

MORE ☎ PRINT

CHARACTER STACK

◁   ▷

DNA ID: HFB2221N888N23

GOTHAM LIFECODES CORP

NAME: SHEILA ROMERO
DOB: UKM
RES: 22 SUTTON PL.
POE: GTHM

PRO: AKA GATA

MORE ☎ PRINT

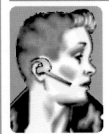

DNA ID: WFE0122N422N24

GOTHAM LIFECODES CORP

NAME: LENA SCHWARTZ
DOB: 10-12-2050
RES: 3025 N 888 ST. 70
POB: MTRPLS

PRO:

MORE   PRINT

DNA ID:

GOTHAM LIFECODES CORP

NAME: MARIA ROMERO
DOB: UKM
RES: MAYOR'S TOWER
POE: GTHM

PRO: AKA MADAM X

MORE ☎ PRINT

DNA ID: OME0212N232N16

GOTHAM LIFECODES CORP

NAME: ROBERT CHANG
DOB: 12-8-2058
RES: 3022 N 900 ST 705
POE: GTHM

PRO: AKA ROBIN

MORE   PRINT

DNA ID:

GOTHAM LIFECODES CORP

NAME: LUKE KRATER
DOB: UKM
RES: GTHM COURT ANNEX
POE: GTHM

PRO: AKA LAW MAN

MORE ☎ PRINT

DNA ID: WME0722N444N74

GOTHAM LIFECODES CORP

NAME: HAROLD GROVER CAPT.
DOB: 1-12-2000
RES: 200 E 50 ST.
POB: HUB CTY

PRO:

MORE   PRINT

DNA ID:

GOTHAM LIFECODES CORP

NAME: HIROSHI BASHO
DOB: UKM
RES: 12 SUTTON PL.
POE: TKO

PRO: AKA MOB LORD

MORE ☎ PRINT

DNA ID: AMB0445N643N71

GOTHAM LIFECODES CORP

NAME: PAUL FAHMY
DOB: 6-25-2003
RES: 4044 NE FLATBUSH AV.
POE: GTHM

PRO: AKA KNOW MAN

MORE   PRINT

DNA ID:

GOTHAM LIFECODES CORP

NAME: JACKIE BECKER
DOB: UKM
RES: MEDIA TOWER
POE: SWOPES CTY

PRO: AKA MEDIA MAN

MORE   PRINT

GLOSSARY STACK

DIGITAL MEDIA

With the Digital De-regulation Act, news reporting became more than just the act of gathering data for dissemination. Earlier Network experiments in "simulating" news events (some as early as the 1970's!) had shown the public's desire for pictorial news. With full digitalization, news executives could edit raw footage to get exactly the images they wanted. Advocates of ethical and responsible news reporting submitted a...

SOURCE   MILLIMETER—JAN. 2011

PREVIOUS   STACKS   MORE

IQ'S

The accidental discovery of IQ-enhancing compounds changed the face of the business world. Despite their addictive properties, they quickly became the **recreational** drug of choice among the affluent, aiding them in their battle up the corporate ladder while producing a phenomenal ego high. Parallels between the spread of "Q"s, as they quickly became known, and anabolic steroids in the 70's and 80's are easy to draw, although...

SOURCE   ENCYCLOPEDIA BRITTANICA—2053

PREVIOUS   STACKS   MORE

MUTAGENICS

Cancer-related DNA research inadvertently led to the creation of MUTAGENICS—drugs that actually changed the DNA/RNA coding in a living body. Through the use of such drugs, individuals could change the very shapes they lived in—an addiction that quickly spread to teenagers and rebellious young adults in the early days of the 21st century...

SOURCE   ENCYCLOPEDIA BRITTANICA—2053

PREVIOUS   STACKS   MORE

PLEASURE SUIT

After tests with completely paralyzed subjects, direct stimulation of the body's pleasure centers through bio-mechanical connection became a reality. Early prototypes, like the California Pleasure Suit of the 1980's, led to hospital, military, and aerospace uses. The sexual experiences achieved are said to be unmatchable in any other way. Unfortunately, widespread usage has led to addiction levels formerly believed impossible...

SOURCE   'THE ART OF CYBER-SEX'— PLAYBOY—JAN. 2050

PREVIOUS   STACKS   MORE

ROBO-PHONE

Early advances in speech recognition technology led to the development of the "smart phone." The idea was to emulate a good personal secretary. The initial prototypes were interesting but generally limited, until the advent of room-temp superconductors. Then, 50 BIP systems became possible, and the first truly intelligent television and Robo-Phones systems became practicable. Later innovations allowed...

SOURCE   BUSINESS WEEK—AUG. 5, 2043

PREVIOUS   STACKS   MORE

SERVO-COP

Breakthrough developments in microelectronics, chip technology, and superconductivity allowed the construction and programming of the first series of Servo Enforcers in 1998. Expert systems combined with high-CPU AI's allowed these Servos to replace human "beat-cops" in the early years of the 21st Century. The introduction of the Model 10 in 2041...

SOURCE   SERVO CORP. STOCKHOLDERS REPORT--MAY 2042

PREVIOUS   STACKS   MORE

SUPERCONDUCTIVITY

Room-temperature superconductivity was finally realized in the Bell Labs in early 1993. This allowed realization of many dreams previously thought impossible.
Computers with Gigabyte Core Storage could now be made smaller than the then-average PC. Anti-Gravity became a reality, and with it, full usage of air space became possible.
The Military-Industrial Complex tried to...

SOURCE   PC WORLD—NOV. 13, 2001—

PREVIOUS   STACKS   MORE

TELEPRESENCE

The Telepresence conferencing system consisted of a video image of the person projected onto a translucent mask of the speaker's face. The "virtual conference" table, as it was called, enabled people in widely separated locations to meet in a situation of "virtual presence." Later developments in holographic technology and the advent of the World-Computer Net allowed for intimate meetings and conferences around the world.

SOURCE   WALL STREET JOURNAL—JAN. 5, 2003

PREVIOUS   STACKS   MORE

DNA ID:

GOTHAM LIFECODES CORP

NAME: BATCOM
DOB: 2020
RES: BATCAVE MAINFRAME
POE: GTHM

PRO: AKA BATCODE

MORE   PRINT

DNA ID:

GOTHAM LIFECODES CORP

NAME: JOKER VIRUS
DOB: 1992
RES: WIRED WORLD
POE: GTHM

PRO: AKA THE JOKER

MORE   PRINT

Pepe Moreno

BIO

Pepe Moreno, a native of Valencia, Spain, began drawing comics as a child and, in his teens, contributed to local horror and underground magazines. After he graduated from high school, he worked for an advertising agency and attended engineering school at night (his father had insisted that he learn a *real* profession). He now realizes that, although they were unwelcome diversions at the time, the agency work and engineering training enabled him to develop his graphic skills.

At age 20 he was drafted into the Spanish army and assigned to a cartography unit in North Africa. After his discharge, he worked briefly as a disc jockey and traveled in Europe and then, in 1977, looking for a new frontier, came to the United States.

To his astonishment, he was quickly offered jobs at DC Comics and Warren Publishing. Because he didn't want to limit himself to drawing super-heroes, he chose to work freelance for Warren. While driving around the country and learning English, he contributed heavily to Warren's horror magazines, **Creepy**, **Eerie**, and **Vampirella**.

Settling in the San Francisco Bay Area, Moreno soon found himself in the middle of the punk movement. In what he felt was his true element at last, he began experimenting with fast, raw, collage-style images on everything from political posters to concert announcements. (This work is discussed in an article in the Fall, 1988 issue of **Design Issues** titled "Rebellion, Reform, and Revolution: American Graphic Design for Social Change" MIT Press). Moreno published NART (No Art), a dadaesque magazine that produced counterculture graphics using a variety of techniques, including what was then the latest technology, the Xerox copier. And he played bass in a punkabilly band.

VALENCIA

Photo: Jeffrey Chong

He also began publishing short pieces in Heavy Metal and Epic Illustrated, the best of which were later collected in **Zeppelin**, and did an ongoing series titled **"Generation Zero"** for Epic. These stories, created, written and illustrated entirely by Moreno, combined his vision of America and the future with a unique color sense and earned him a devoted following, especially in Europe, where they were widely reprinted.

In 1982, Moreno packed his belongings into a red 1967 Cadillac and drove to New York. Stimulated by that energetic city, he quickly completed three much-acclaimed graphic novels, **Rebel**, **Joe's Air Force,** and **Gene Kong**. Working in the longer novel format, he began to think of comics as "movies on paper," and that led him into animation. He designed high-tech, futuristic sets and mutated characters for three nationally-syndicated television series, "Tiger Sharks," "Thunder Cats" and "Silver Hawks" and directed animated portions of television commercials.

In the last few years, Moreno has been fascinated with sophisticated personal computers (first the Amiga and later the Mac II). When high-resolution became available, he decided to combine his art with his computer expertise; he has been on the cutting edge of graphics technology ever since. He serves as a consultant on art and illustration software packages for several major companies and his computer-generated illustrations were featured in "Technology in the Year 2000" (Fortune, July 18, 1988). In 1989, he won the Macintosh Masters contest in the illustration category.

Moreno is certain that multi-media, digital entertainment is the wave of the future. He plans to be at the forefront of it.

TECHNICAL SUPPORT

HARDWARE

SOFTWARE

ELECTRONIC ARTS

Luc Barthelet

Nic Lavroff

Nicole Nolan

ANAYA SYSTEMS

Marcel Coderch

ENABLING

TECHNOLOGIES

Melissa Teller

Joe Grossman

LETRASET

Lisa Wellman

SILICON BEACH

Stuart Genigson

WEISS WORKS

David Cody Weiss

SHARP INC.

Mark Albanese

THE RADIUS CORP.

Steve Becker

RASTER OPS

Richard James

THANKS TO:

Charis Moe

Melissa Schwarz

Alex Arce

Apple Computers